G000123997

KS2
English
Practice Test Papers

Ages 7-11

John Goulding

Contents

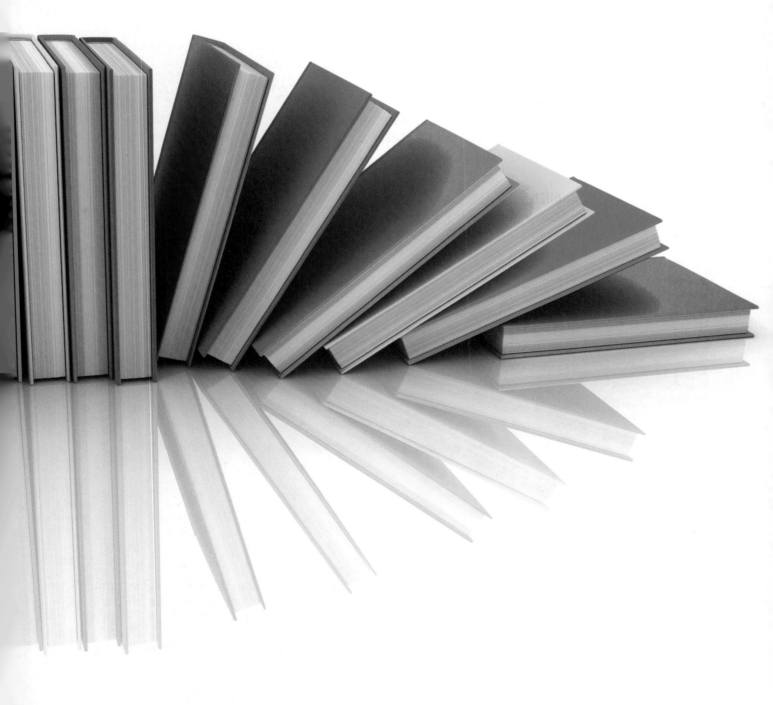

Sets
A&B

KEY STAGE 2
Levels 3–5
Introduction

English

Introduction

Introduction

Instructions on using
the Practice Test Papers

Understanding Assessment

What is assessment?
Teacher assessment and national test results are used to determine your child's level of attainment at the end of Key Stage 2 (at the age of 11).

What are the children tested and assessed on?
The national tests are designed to test children's knowledge and understanding of specific elements of the Key Stage 2 curriculum in English and Maths. This is a typical breakdown of the tests:

English
Reading (45 minutes + 15 minutes reading time)
Writing Long Test 45 minutes and Short Test 20 minutes
Spelling 10 minutes
Handwriting

Maths
Mental Maths (20 minutes)
Written paper (45 minutes)
Written paper (45 minutes)

Pupils at some schools also take part in Science sampling tests. However, this is simply used to monitor national standards.

Your child's teacher will also assess their learning at other times. Teacher assessment covers:

- English
- Maths
- Science.

What do the English tests assess in my child?
In the Reading Test your child is assessed against seven different Assessment Focus (AF) criteria. These take into account a range of aspects of your child's reading which are assessed in school tests:

AF1   Use a range of strategies, including accurate decoding of text, to read for meaning.

AF2   Understand, describe, select or retrieve information, events or ideas from texts, and use quotations and references to text.

AF3   Deduce, infer or interpret information, events or ideas from texts.

AF4   Identify and comment on the structure and organisation of texts, including grammatical and presentational features at text level.

AF5   Explain and comment on the writers' use of language, including grammatical and literary features at word and sentence level.

AF6   Identify and comment on the writers' purposes and viewpoints, and the overall effect of text on the reader.

AF7   Relate texts to their social, cultural and historical contexts and literary traditions.

(Source: QCDA 2011 mark scheme)

How these Tests will Help your Child

1   These test papers are similar to the ones your child will take at the end of Year 6. The papers provide a good idea of the strengths and weaknesses of your child's subject knowledge.

2   The Answers and Mark Scheme have been provided to allow you to check how your child has done.

3   When an area of weakness has been identified, it is useful to go over these and similar types of questions with your child. Sometimes your child will be familiar with the subject matter but might not understand what the question is asking. This will become apparent when talking to your child.

Tips for the Top

1   **Don't make silly mistakes**. Make sure you emphasise to your child the importance of reading the question. Easy marks can be picked up by just doing as the question asks.

2   **Make your answers clearly legible**. If your child has made a mistake, encourage them to put a cross through it and write the correct answer clearly next to it. Try to encourage your child to use an eraser as little as possible.

3   **Don't panic**! These practice test papers, and indeed the end of Key Stage 2 tests, are meant to provide teachers with a guide to the level a child has attained. They are not the be-all and end-all, as children are assessed regularly throughout the school year. Explain to your child that there is no need to worry if they cannot do a question, just go on to the next question and come back to it later if they have time.

Instructions for Parents

1   Make sure you provide your child with a quiet environment where they can complete their test undisturbed.

2   Provide your child with the following equipment: pencil, ruler and eraser (rubber).

3   The test papers vary in the amount of time given so always consult the front page of each paper. The Reading Tests are both 1 hour long. Your child should be given 15 minutes to read through the Reading Material and 45 minutes to answer the questions. The Long Writing Tests are both 45 minutes long and the Short Writing Tests are both 20 minutes long.

4   You may only read the instructions to your child.

Reading Test

Although each Assessment Focus is tested, you should note that AF1 is not done so separately. By the end of Key Stage 2 it is expected that your child is using "a range of strategies, including accurate decoding of text, to read for meaning". The majority of questions in the Reading Test are concerned with AF3.

In the Answers and Mark Scheme for each Reading Test, the AF is identified for each question. On marking each paper, these will help you and your child to identify areas of strength and weakness in their comprehension skills. When your child is reading you will then be able to devise questions similar to those for each AF and develop comprehension skills in this way.

Before marking the Reading Test, ensure that you read the Reading Material for that test. This will help to clarify the mark scheme and will also help you to judge whether the content of an answer is correct. Different children have different ways of wording a correct answer – you need to judge whether your child "had the right idea".

Administering the Reading Test

Your child should be provided with a pen or pencil with which to write.

The Reading Test does not assess the child's handwriting or spelling but children should be reminded that their answers must be clear.

Your child should begin by reading through the Reading Material for approximately 15 minutes and then answering the questions in a further 45 minutes.

Your child can re-read and refer back to the Reading Material whenever they need to.

Writing Test

There are four elements to the Writing Test:
1   Long Writing Test
2   Short Writing Test
3   Handwriting (incorporated in the Long Writing Test)
4   Spelling

The Long and Short Writing Test and the Handwriting are covered by six Mark Strands (A to F). Each Strand is divided into a number of Bands. When a test paper is marked the marker decides, from a range of statements, into which Band a piece of writing falls. In the Answers and Mark Scheme, the statements have been turned into questions which you and your child can answer together.

It is important to read the piece of writing at least twice before you attempt to apply it to any of the Bands. This will enable you to gain a good, general feel for the content and quality.

Using the Answers and Mark Scheme, you should be able to build up a picture of the Bands within which your child is working. You may notice that your child's Band for grammar and punctuation is different from their Band for "organising" or "telling" the story. It is possible to achieve different Bands for each of the Mark Strands.

If your child is producing writing that falls within the final Band of each Mark Strand with some consistency, then it is likely that they are working at a standard of high level 5 or beyond. It is also possible that, for writing, they could be classed as Gifted or Talented by their school.

By analysing writing with your child in such detail, you will both be able to see what they do well and where their writing needs to develop. Use the questions in each Band as targets and guidance when your child is next planning and writing another text. Familiarity with the requirements of the Writing Test are very important and targeting specific areas will develop your child's writing skills.

Administering the Writing Tests

Your child should be provided with lined paper and a pen or pencil with which to write.

For the Long Test they should be reminded that their handwriting will also be assessed. They will have 45 minutes in total. The task may be read to them and they should then aim to spend approximately 10 minutes planning and 35 minutes writing. For the Short Test they will have 20 minutes in total, of which approximately 5 minutes should be used for planning time.

Administering the Spelling Test

The Spelling Test consists of a short passage which should be read twice in its entirety to the child taking the test. During the first reading, the child should not write anything on their answer sheet. During the second reading, the reader should pause after each word to be tested (in bold type) to enable the child to write the word into the gap on their answer sheet.

The complete passages for Set A and Set B Spelling Tests are on page 102.

Marking the Tests and Assessing Levels

1   Make sure your child has completed all the relevant tests, e.g. Set A Reading Paper, Set A Long Writing Test Paper, Set A Short Writing Test Paper and Set A Spelling Test Paper.

2   Mark the practice test papers using the mark scheme and samples in the pull-out Answers and Mark Scheme.

3   Add up the marks on each paper. The Reading Test Paper is marked out of 50 and the Writing is marked out of 50. This gives a maximum total of 100 marks.

4   Write the marks in the marking grid below.

Section	Marks available	Set A score	Set B score
Reading Scores			
Reading Test	50		
Writing Scores			
Long Writing Test – sentence structure and punctuation (Strand A)	8		
Long Writing Test – text structure and organisation (Strand B)	8		
Long Writing Test – composition and effect (Strand C)	12		
Handwriting (Strand F)	3		
Short Writing Test – sentence structure, punctuation and text organisation (Strand D)	4		
Short Writing Test – composition and effect (Strand E)	8		
Spelling Test	7		
Total Writing Score	50		
Combined English Score	100		

Curriculum Levels

Reading level

Below Level 3	Level 3	Level 4	Level 5	High Level 5
up to 10	11–22	23–35	36–45	46+

Writing level

Below Level 3	Level 3	Level 4	Level 5	High Level 5
up to 18	19–30	31–38	39–47	48+

Combined English level

Below Level 3	Level 3	Level 4	Level 5	High Level 5
up to 29	30–53	54–74	75–93	94+

Please note: these tests are **only a guide** to the level your child can achieve and cannot guarantee the same level is achieved at Key Stage 2.

Shared Marking and Target Setting

Engaging your child in the marking process with you will help them to develop a greater understanding of the English Tests and, more importantly, provide them with some ownership of their learning. They will be able to see more clearly how and why certain areas have been identified for them to target for improvement.

What do the levels mean?

When your child's English papers are marked, the correct marks are collated to give your child an overall score. This score is then matched to a National Curriculum level.

At the end of Key Stage 2, most students (80%) are expected to achieve Level 4 and approximately 35% of students will reach Level 5.

Tips for Improvement

Reading Tips for Parents

Once you have assessed your child's level using the Set A Reading Test Paper, use the techniques below to help them develop their reading skills. Then test your child again using the Set B Reading Test Paper.

1   Share a wide range of texts (both fiction and non-fiction) with your child, taking it in turns to read sections and discuss the themes, ideas, language features and presentational features.

2   Encourage your child to read each day.

3   Encourage your child to read a variety of texts (different genres and authors).

4   Model good practice – let your child see you reading and enjoying it.

5   When your child has completed each practice test paper in this book, share the marking with them and discuss their answers in depth.

6   Model how to find the correct answers.

7   Discuss the Assessment Focuses for reading (see pages 4–5).

8   Ask your child several questions about any text they are reading (these questions could be based on the Assessment Focuses).

9   Provide your child with lots of positive encouragement – they will respond well to it.

Reading Tips for Children

Try the techniques below to help you improve weak areas.

Before the test

Make sure you read a variety of good quality fiction and non-fiction texts (these will also help to give you ideas of different styles for your Writing Paper).

Get into the habit of reading each day.

Even if you are a good reader, read with an adult whenever you can and ask the adult to ask you lots of questions about the text. Both you and an adult can familiarise yourself with the Assessment Focuses on which you will be tested (see pages 4–5).

Work through practice papers (like the ones in this book) to get used to the timing of the test and the question types.

Make up and answer your own questions about a text – really try to understand the characters, the story (or the subject) and why the author has written in a particular style (again use the Assessment Focuses to help you).

During the test

Read through the Reading Material very carefully.

When reading through the Reading Material, underline the important information in the text. Use brief notes or your own code for highlighting main characters, key facts, main parts of the text and changes in scene or subject.

Ensure   you always read each question very carefully.

Always   refer back to the text for relevant information.

Complete   each question – don't miss any out. No answer – NO MARK!

Check   your answers again if there is time.

Spelling Tips for Parents

Once you have assessed your child's level using the Set A Spelling Test Paper, use the information below to help them develop their skills in spelling. Then test your child again using the Set B Spelling Test Paper.

The Literacy Strategy sets out words that children should learn each year they are in primary school. You should check your child knows the Key Stage 2 words. Spelling is best learnt when both phonic strategies (sound) and visual strategies (recognising groups of letters) are used.

In the early stages of learning to spell, children should learn to memorise short common words, e.g. *get, went*. Then they should learn to match sounds to letters – this should help them to spell simple words.

As your child becomes more aware of the relationship between sounds and letters, you should help them to see that patterns exist. These include:

1   the effect of doubling the vowel, e.g. "ee" as in **sheep, sleep, freeze**

2   how certain vowels and consonants combine, e.g. "ar" as in **car, card, hard**

3   how some consonants combine to make particular sounds, e.g. "ch" as in **chain, choice, chase**

4   how a silent 'e' affects the vowel, e.g. **hop/hope, bit/bite, car/care**

5   how two vowels combine to give a particular sound, e.g. "oi" as in **oil, boil, toil**

6   how the grouping of two or more letters gives a particular sound, e.g. "igh" as in **sigh, high, slight**

7   how words that have long vowel sounds, such as **journey**, need to be committed to visual memory

8   how words with double consonants need to be memorised, e.g. **commented**

Please note that these are just a selection of patterns and strategies. There are more and if you have concerns about your child's spelling, do not hesitate to raise the issue with their teacher.

Spelling Tips for Children

Try the techniques below to help you improve weak areas.

It is a good idea to practise memorising how words "look" and the letter sequences in more complex words. You need to get used to considering whether a word "looks right".

A useful way to help you to memorise a spelling is to use the routine of "Look, Cover, Write, Check".

Look   Look at a word and identify phonic patterns (sound patterns) or sequences of letters within the word.

Cover   Cover the word but try to memorise the spelling.

Write   Write the spelling down.

Check   Check whether the written word is spelt correctly, identify any mistakes, then try again.

Set

A

KEY STAGE 2
Levels 3–5

Reading
Test Paper

English

On Track

Reading Test Paper

On Track

Instructions:

- find a quiet place where you can sit down and complete the test paper undisturbed
- make sure you have all the necessary equipment to complete the test paper
- read the questions carefully
- answer all the questions in this test paper
- go through and check your answers when you have finished the test paper

Time:

This test paper is **1 hour** long.

You should ensure you spend **15 minutes** reading through the Reading Material on pages 15–26 before you begin the test. Do not worry if you have not read all the Reading Material in this time, because you can (and should) look at it as many times as you like during the test.

The main written part of the test should take **45 minutes**. There are several question types:

Multiple choice	you put a ring around the correct option
Short answers	requiring only a word or short phrase
Several line answers	these questions require you to write more than a single point
Explanation answers	you are required to write an answer and explain it, often in quite a lot of detail and with evidence from the text
Other answers	you may be required to draw lines connecting related words

Check how your child has done against the Answers and Mark Scheme on pages 81–83.

Page	27	29	31	33	35	37	Max. Mark	**Actual Mark**
Score	....	....	....	....	....	....	50	....

First name _____

Last name _____

ON TRACK

Contents

Introduction

Since the early nineteenth century, people have had a fascination with trains and rail travel. From the early trains to the present day, this mode of transport has played a huge role in the daily life of nations around the globe.

Due to rail travel, trade and industry changed as it provided a faster way to transport large quantities of goods and materials. Our lives changed, because of the ease with which we could visit new and distant places with greater speed than ever before.

The railway age has influenced many books and films. *The Railway Children* is one such book. Written at the beginning of the twentieth century, it has also been turned into several film versions. You can read an extract from the book and all about the films on the following pages.

Other information here provides a brief history of the development of rail travel and an insight into The Orient Express, considered by many to be the world's most luxurious train.

After their father goes away unexpectedly, Bobbie, Peter and Phyllis move to the countryside with their mother. They leave behind their life in London to live in a small cottage called Three Chimneys.

They had lived all their lives in a street where cabs and omnibuses rumbled by at all hours, and the carts of butchers and bakers and candlestick makers might occur at any moment. Here in the deep silence of the sleeping country the only things that went by were the trains. They seemed to be all that was left to link the children to the old life that had once been theirs. Straight down the hill in front of Three Chimneys the daily passage of their six feet began to mark a path across the crisp, short turf. They began to know the hours when certain trains passed, and they gave names to them. The 9.15 up was called the Green Dragon. The 10.07 down was the Worm of Wantley. The midnight town express, whose shrieking rush they sometimes woke from their dreams to hear, was the Fearsome Fly-by-night. Peter got up once, in chill starshine, and, peeping at it through his curtains, named it on the spot.

It was by the Green Dragon that the old gentleman travelled. He was a very nice-looking old gentleman, and he looked as if he were nice, too, which is not at all the same thing. He had a fresh-coloured, clean-shaven face and white hair, and he wore rather odd-shaped collars and a top-hat that wasn't exactly the same kind as other people's. Of course the children didn't see all this at first. In fact the first thing they noticed about the old gentleman was his hand.

The

It was one morning as they sat on the fence waiting for the Green Dragon, which was three and a quarter minutes late by Peter's Waterbury watch that he had had given him on his last birthday.

"The Green Dragon's going where Father is," said Phyllis; "if it were a really real dragon, we could stop it and ask it to take our love to Father."

"Dragons don't carry people's love," said Peter; "they'd be above it."

"Yes, they do, if you tame them thoroughly first. They fetch and carry like pet spaniels," said Phyllis, "and feed out of your hand. I wonder why Father never writes to us."

"Mother says he's been too busy," said Bobbie, "but he'll write soon, she says."

"I say," Phyllis suggested, "let's all wave to the Green Dragon as it goes by. If it's a magic dragon, it'll understand and take our loves to Father. And if it isn't, three waves aren't much. We shall never miss them."

So when the Green Dragon tore shrieking out of the mouth of its dark lair, which was the tunnel, all three children stood on the railing and waved their pocket-handkerchiefs without stopping to think whether they were clean handkerchiefs or the reverse. They were, as a matter of fact, very much the reverse.

And out of a first-class carriage a hand waved back. A quite clean hand. It held a newspaper. It was the old gentleman's hand.

After this it became the custom for waves to be exchanged between the children and the 9.15.

And the children, especially the girls, liked to think that perhaps the old gentleman knew Father, and would meet him "in business", wherever that shady retreat might be, and tell him how his three children stood on a rail far away in the green country and waved their love to him every morning, wet or fine.

From *The Railway Children* by Edith Nesbit

Green Dragon
nd the Old Gentleman

The Railway
From Book to Screen

The book

The Railway Children tells the tale of Roberta, Peter and Phyllis as they embark on a series of adventures. They are forced to move to a country cottage when their father unexpectedly goes away from their London home. In their new surroundings they become fascinated by the nearby railway and meet many new friends as they wonder where their father is and whether he will ever return.

Author Edith Nesbit based some of the ideas in the story on her own experiences. Her first children's book, *The Treasure Seekers*, was published in 1899. *The Railway Children* was published seven years later in 1906 and is still extremely popular today.

Children

On screen

The Railway Children was first shown in 1968 as a six-part serial on BBC television. The serial was made in black and white. A 16 year-old girl called Jenny Agutter played the role of Roberta (Bobbie).

In 1970 the story was released in a very well-known film version, this time in colour. Again the role of Bobbie was played by Jenny Agutter.

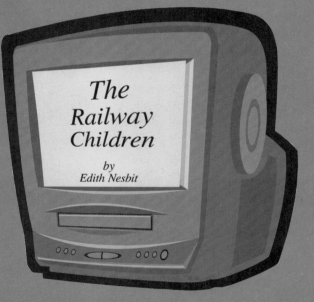

The first showing (the premiere) took place in London in 1970 with special guests including Her Royal Highness Princess Margaret, accompanied by her nephews Prince Andrew and Prince Edward.

At Christmas 1970, it was shown privately to the Queen and other members of the Royal Family at Windsor Castle.

The British Film Institute has voted *The Railway Children* among the best one hundred British pictures of the past century. It has also been included in the Chicago Museum of Fine Arts as an example of fine British film making.

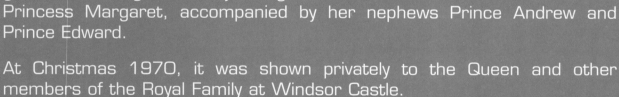

In 2000, a new film version was released. This immediately proved very popular with old and new fans alike. The role of Bobbie was this time played by Jemima Rooper, but there remained a strong link with the original film; the mother was played by Jenny Agutter.

An Interview With the Railway Children

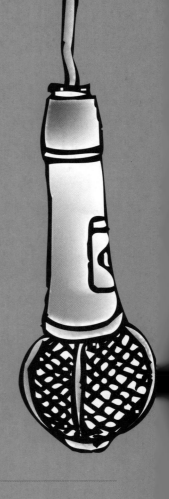

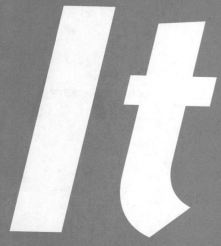**It** was a rather wet and dismal Thursday when I went to the set of *The Railway Children* (2000 film) at Horsted Keynes in Sussex to meet the three young stars of the production, Jemima, Jack and Clare.

They were sitting in a caravan in their Edwardian costumes looking just like children from another world, but talking very much like the modern children they are.

Have you read E. Nesbit's book?

Jemima: I read it when I was very young as it's one of those classic books everyone reads. I read it again when I was auditioning for the part of Bobbie so I could research the character.

Clare: I once started to read it but didn't finish it but then, when I got the part of Phyllis, I had to complete a book-reading exercise for school so I read it then.

Jack: I haven't read it all, but I have heard it on tape and I've seen the 1970 film.

Have you found your characters easy to play?

Jemima: I do now but at first I was worried, because playing a twelve year-old in the early 1900s is very different. They were very much children then until they were quite a lot older.

Clare: Phyllis is pretty easy to play, because she's quite young and hasn't learnt much about the world yet. She doesn't have any major speeches using large, old-fashioned words.

Jack: Playing Peter is quite straightforward. I think he's trying to be grown up and be the man of the house. He's not really that big, but would like to take control.

Have you noticed any similarities between your characters and yourselves?

Jemima: Bobbie is lovely and she's one of those people you admire and want to be like. She is very sweet and gentle with her brother and sister. She's very amusing trying to be adult and mature. I'd like to think we were similar, but really I don't think so! Jack, Clare and I feel like real brother and sisters, which is nice. I definitely feel like their older sister. But no, I don't think I'm really like Bobbie at all.

Did wearing the period costumes help towards playing the character?

Jemima: Absolutely! It really, really helps! The minute you've got your costume on your movements are restricted. It makes me feel like a little doll, which makes me feel younger and helps with the part.

Jack: Most of the costumes are alright, but at the moment I am having problems with this stiff collar! It's kind of hard to breathe sometimes. I think wearing the costumes does help you to focus.

At this point a member of the production team entered the caravan and called the children out into the damp morning, ready to bring to life another scene from E. Nesbit's classic story.

The interviewer was Pete Coleman

For centuries, the fastest way of travelling was on horseback. Long-distance travel meant many days, many rests and often many changes of horse. People rarely travelled more than a few kilometres from their homes and very few visited other towns or villages.

When railways came along in the 1800s, all of this changed. Travel became quick and convenient. Major towns and cities throughout Great Britain and the rest of Europe became easy to reach in just a few hours. People could move around the world as never before and trains became as popular then as air travel is today.

The world's first public steam railway, just 40 km of track in north-east England, was soon followed by larger networks and rail travel opened up new horizons for everyone. People started to make day trips, with the seaside especially popular, and large continents could be crossed in just a few days rather than months.

Fact Box

- Longest railway network – the USA with 240,000 km

- Longest railway – the Trans-Siberian line from Moscow to Vladivostok (9,611 km)

- Longest straight track – 478 km in south-western Australia

1804 Richard Trevithick tests the first steam locomotive in Wales.

1825 The Stockton to Darlington Railway opens using steam locomotives.

1863 The world's first underground passenger railway opens in London.

1883 The Orient Express first runs from Paris to Bucharest.

World

Speeding into the future

The first trains were powered by steam. In 1829, the Rocket could average 24 km per hour. Soon, however, bigger and faster steam locomotives came along. In the 1870s the Stirling Single could reach speeds of 129 km per hour and in 1893, an American locomotive was said to have travelled at 160 km per hour.

Another famous British train, the Mallard, reached 203 km per hour in 1938. By now, though, diesel and electrically powered trains were also becoming popular. The age of steam was slowly coming to an end.

From Rocket ...

The Rocket was the brainchild of Robert and George Stephenson. In 1829, the Rainhill Trials were held to find the best locomotive for the Liverpool to Manchester railway. It convinced people that steam locomotives were the future of transport.

... to Bullet

The Bullet entered service in 1964, running between Tokyo and Osaka in Japan. Shaped more like a bullet than a train, the latest version reaches speeds of 300 km per hour (186 mph).

1938 The Mallard sets the world speed record of 203 km per hour.

1964 The Bullet enters service in Japan.

1981 The high speed French TGV enters service between Paris and Lyon.

1994 The 50 km long Channel Tunnel is completed, linking Britain with the rest of Europe.

The Venice Simplon Orient Express is the most famous luxury train in the world. It has been used by the rich and famous since its first journey in 1883. Glamour, elegance and style apply to both the train and its passengers.

On board, passengers have their own personal stewards attending to their every need. Wood-panelled compartments provide private sitting rooms by day and luxurious bedrooms by night.

A dining car is laid out with the finest crystal glasses, table linen and cutlery awaiting the service of wonderful food produced by French chefs.

In the evening, passengers wearing fine gowns and suits gather to sip drinks as they chat or listen to the piano in the bar.

All this takes place as the train snakes its way across Europe and if the quality of life inside the train becomes too much, the passengers can simply look through the window at some of the finest scenery the continent has to offer.

A journey on the Orient Express is a journey on which standards are beyond the ordinary. Wealthy passengers travel in luxury through a rich and varied landscape on what is seen by many to be the most romantic journey in the world.

Travelling in Style

Section 1

These questions are about the fiction passage "The Green Dragon and the Old Gentleman" on pages 18–19.

Choose the best word or group of words and put a ring around your choice.   (*1 mark*)

Q1

1   The old gentleman travelled on:

the midnight town express.

the Green Dragon.

the 10.07 down.

the Fearsome Fly-by-night.

2   The first thing the children noticed about the old gentleman was: (*1 mark*)

Q2

his hat.

his newspaper.

his hand.

his white hair.

3   Phyllis suggested that they all: (*1 mark*)

Q3

watch for trains.

go to the station.

wave to the old man.

wave to the Green Dragon.

subtotal

4 The children liked to think that the old gentleman would: *(1 mark)*

   take their love to father.

   wave to them.

   be their friend.

   be kind to them.

5 Phyllis told the others that dragons: *(1 mark)*

   could be fierce creatures.

   could be treated like a pet.

   are easy to train.

   knew their father.

6 The trains ... *seemed to be all that was left to link the children to the old life that*
   had once been theirs. Give two reasons why the trains provided this link. *(2 marks)*

   a) _____

       _____

       _____

   b) _____

       _____

       _____

7   *... when the Green Dragon tore shrieking out of the mouth of its dark lair ...*

Why does the author use these words to describe the dragon coming
out of the tunnel?

(2 marks)

Q7

_____

_____

_____

_____

8   How can you tell that the children are missing their father?

Explain fully, using the text to help you.

(3 marks)

Q8

_____

_____

_____

_____

_____

_____

subtotal

9   When the children waved at the train they used their pocket-handkerchiefs.

a) Why did they wave with their handkerchiefs?   (1 mark)

Q9a

_____

_____

_____

b) Why do you think they did not stop ... *to think whether they were clean handkerchiefs?*   (1 mark)

Q9b

_____

_____

_____

10   *"Mother says he's been too busy," said Bobbie, "but he'll write soon, she says."*

Explain what this tells us about Bobbie's relationship with her brother and sister.
(1 mark)

Q10

_____

_____

_____

Section 2

These questions are about the information in "*The Railway Children –
From Book to Screen*" on pages 20–21.

11 Why has the title "*The Railway Children* – From Book to Screen" been chosen for
this short, informative text?   *(1 mark)*

Q11

_____

_____

_____

12 What is the purpose of this piece of text?   *(1 mark)*

Q12

_____

_____

_____

13 The text shows that the 1970 film version of *The Railway Children* was very highly
thought of. Select two pieces of information in the text that show this.   *(2 marks)*

Q13

a) _____

_____

_____

b) _____

_____

_____

subtotal

Section 3

These questions are about the text "An Interview With the Railway Children" on page 23.

14 Jemima tells us that she finds her character easy to play, but *"... at first I was worried, because playing a twelve year-old in the early 1900s is very different. They were very much children then until they were quite a lot older."*

What does she mean by
"They were very much children then until they were quite a lot older"?   (2 marks)

Q1

_____

_____

_____

_____

15 Why are the children described as
"... looking just like children from another world"?   (1 mark)

Q1

_____

_____

_____

16 How does Jemima think that wearing her costume helps her to play the part of Bobbie?   (1 mark)

Q1

_____

_____

_____

Section 4

17 The title of the section on pages 24 and 25 is "A Small World".

Explain why this is a suitable title for this section. *(3 marks)* ☐ Q17

_____

_____

_____

_____

_____

_____

_____

18 Put the following information in the correct order. The first one has been done for you.

(2 marks) ☐ Q18

The Japanese Bullet train makes its first journey ☐
The Rocket wins the Rainhill Trials ☐
The Mallard sets the world record ☐
Trevithick tests the first steam locomotive 1

19 Having read this text, why do you think the age of steam
   eventually came to an end? *(1 mark)*

Q19

_____

_____

_____

20 Most of the information on the timeline (at the bottom of pages 24 and 25) is
   already included in the other text on these pages.

   Why has the timeline been included? *(2 marks)*

Q2

_____

_____

_____

_____

21 Why do you think the author has used the two connected passages
   From Rocket ... to Bullet? *(1 mark)*

Q2

_____

_____

_____

Section 5

These questions are about the text "Travelling in Style" on page 26.

22 The Orient Express has many luxuries. According to the text, where can these luxuries be found on the train? The first one has been done for you.   *(2 marks)*   ☐ Q22

a piano   in the compartments

wood panelling   in the dining car

fine views ――――――   in the bar

finest crystal glasses   ――――→ through the windows

23 Why does the author use the word "snakes" to describe the train's journey across Europe?

(2 marks)   ☐ Q23

_____

_____

_____

24 In the final sentence, which four separate words emphasise the quality of a journey on the Orient Express?

(2 marks)   ☐ Q24

_____ _____ _____ _____

25 If you were a passenger on the Orient Express, who would you ask if you needed anything?

(1 mark)   ☐ Q25

_____

_____

subtotal

Section 6

26 Do you think children today have as much fascination with trains as the three children in *The Railway Children*?

Explain your opinion.

(2 marks)

Q2

_____

_____

_____

_____

27 Why do you think the article "Travelling in Style" has been included at the end of the Reading Material?

(2 marks)

Q2

_____

_____

_____

_____

28 The title of the Reading Material is "On Track". For what reason do you think this title was chosen?

(2 marks)

Q2

_____

_____

29 The text "An Interview With the Railway Children" is adapted from a website all about the film, the characters and the trains.

For what reason might such a website exist? *(2 marks)*

_____

_____

_____

_____

_____

30 Why do you think this Reading Material contains information about *The Railway Children* (including a passage from the book) as well as information about trains and rail travel? *(3 marks)*

_____

_____

_____

_____

_____

_____

END OF TEST

subtotal

TEST ADVICE

This information will not appear in school tests.
It is included here to remind you not to stop working
until you are told the 1 hour test is over.

Check your answers again if there is time.

DO NOT JUST SIT THERE WHEN FINISHED

FINDING ONE MISTAKE CAN MEAN EXTRA MARKS.
IT MAY ONLY TAKE 1 MARK TO MOVE UP TO THE NEXT LEVEL.

DO YOUR BEST and DO NOT PANIC.

Set
A

KEY STAGE 2
Levels 3–5

Long Writing
Test Paper

English

A Peculiar Incident

Long Writing Test Paper

A Peculiar Incident

Instructions:

- find a quiet place where you can sit down and complete the test paper undisturbed
- make sure you have all the necessary equipment to complete the test paper
- read the question carefully
- answer the question on lined paper
- go through and check your answer when you have finished writing

Time:

This test paper is **45 minutes** long. This includes planning and writing time. Aim to spend approximately **10 minutes** planning your writing using the planning prompts.

Check how your child has done against the Answers and Mark Scheme on pages 87–101.

	Max. Mark	**Actual Mark**
Score	31	....

First name ....

Last name ....

A Peculiar Incident

The Ghost Train ride was more funny than spooky. That was until the moment we came out of the dark and back into the fairground. Nothing was the same. Everything had changed.

Your task is to write a story based on this idea.

You should think about these things:

1   The characters in the story.

2   What has changed.

3   What happened next.

4   The ending of the story.

Planning

Write useful words and phrases to help you develop the story. These notes will not be marked.

Beginning

Middle

End

Set A

KEY STAGE 2
Levels 3–5

Short Writing
Test Paper

English

Fun-tastic Express

Short Writing Test Paper

Fun-tastic Express

Instructions:

- find a quiet place where you can sit down and complete the test paper undisturbed
- make sure you have all the necessary equipment to complete the test paper
- read the question carefully
- answer the question on lined paper
- go through and check your answer when you have finished writing

Time:

This test paper is **20 minutes** long. This includes planning and writing time. Aim to spend approximately **5 minutes** planning your writing using the planning prompts.

Check how your child has done against the Answers and Mark Scheme on pages 87–101.

	Max. Mark	**Actual Mark**
Score	12	....

First name   ....

Last name   ....

Fun-tastic Express

A new train providing entertainment for children as it visits major towns and cities has just started to operate. The activities on offer are:

1   a magician

2   an adventure playground

3   a ball pool

4   a mini-rollercoaster.

The Fun-tastic Express wants a display in the nearest railway station to your school.

Imagine you have been on the Fun-tastic Express and write a review of your favourite activity for the display.

Planning

Before you start, briefly consider these things. These notes will not be marked.

The activity you enjoyed most and why

Key words to describe the activity

Set
A

KEY STAGE 2
Levels 3–5

Spelling
Test Paper

English

Spelling Test Paper

Belgian Connection

Instructions to parents:

- find a quiet place where you can sit down with your child

- make sure you have all the necessary equipment to complete the test paper

- read the short piece of text on page 102 to your child twice in its entirety

- during the first reading, your child should not write anything on the answer sheet

- during the second reading, pause after each word to be tested (shown in bold type), to enable your child to write the word in the gap on the answer sheet

- check how your child has done against the passage on page 102

	Max.	Number of words correct
Score	20	....

See page 103 for the spelling test mark conversion chart.

First name ....

Last name ....

Belgian Connection

Belgian Connection

In 1815 the Duke of Wellington _____ the French army of

Napoleon near the _____ of Waterloo, a few kilometres from

Brussels in Belgium.

The Battle of Waterloo was not only _____ as a great

_____ for the British but it also gave its name to a

_____ London railway station.

Waterloo station was _____ on 11 July 1848 by London South West

Railway. Over the _____ 50 years many more parts were added as a

result of the _____ increase in the number of railway lines.

_____ 1902 and 1922 the station was completely rebuilt and had

its _____ opening in March 1922. A Victory Arch, representing

war and _____ , was _____ into the

façade. This commemorated workers who died in World War I.

As the _____ century came to a close, Waterloo was

_____ as it became London's main _____ with the

railways of Europe _____ the Channel Tunnel. The station

_____ the largest roof area of any railway station in the UK and has

shops, food outlets and even a _____. Remarkably, the station now

also has a new link with Belgium. _____ day the Eurostar

_____ runs up to nine trains a day from London Waterloo

to Brussels.

Set

B

KEY STAGE 2
Levels 3–5

Reading Test
Paper

English

Polar Explorer

Reading Test Paper

Polar Explorer

Instructions:

- find a quiet place where you can sit down and complete the test paper undisturbed
- make sure you have all the necessary equipment to complete the test paper
- read the questions carefully
- answer all the questions in this test paper
- go through and check your answers when you have finished the test paper

Time:

This test paper is **1 hour** long.

You should ensure you spend **15 minutes** reading through the Reading Material on pages 49–58 before you begin the test. Do not worry if you have not read all the Reading Material in this time, because you can (and should) look at it as many times as you like during the test.

The main written part of the test should take **45 minutes**. There are several question types:

Multiple choice	you put a ring around the correct option
Short answers	requiring only a word or short phrase
Several line answers	these questions require you to write more than a single point
Explanation answers	you are required to write an answer and explain it, often in quite a lot of detail and with evidence from the text
Other answers	you may be required to draw lines connecting related words

Check how your child has done against the Answers and Mark Scheme on pages 84–86.

Page	59	61	63	65	67	69	70	Max. Mark	**Actual Mark**
Score	....	....	....	....	....	....	....	50	....

First name _____

Last name _____

POLAR EXPLORER

Contents

Introduction

The Arctic and Antarctic regions in general, and the North and South Poles in particular, have long intrigued explorers and adventurers.

In the early years of the twentieth century, there were determined efforts to be the first to reach the Poles and even modern explorers find new challenges in these icy wilderness areas.

On the following pages, you are given a flavour of what the polar regions of our planet are like in *Pole to Pole*. There are also articles on three polar explorers, covering the race to the South Pole and more modern polar exploration. Finally, the poem *Explorer* looks at the way a cat might explore a snow-covered garden.

Pole to Pole

The polar regions are the extremely cold areas found to the far north and south of our planet. They are considered to be among the most inhospitable places on Earth and were the last large areas on Earth to be explored.

The Arctic

The northern polar region is known as the Arctic. This is a huge ocean surrounded by land. The North Pole (the most northerly point on Earth) is in this ocean. However, it is possible to get to the North Pole on foot, because a large proportion of the ocean remains frozen all year round.

During the Arctic winter, the sun never rises and during the summer it never sets, although it remains low in the sky and is therefore very weak.

Although people live on the land at the edge of the Arctic Ocean, they do not live at the North Pole because the ice is floating and moving.

The Antarctic

The Antarctic is the southern polar region and the South Pole can be found here. Unlike the North Pole, the South Pole is completely surrounded by land.

As with the Arctic, the sun never rises during an Antarctic winter and remains close to the horizon during the summer. However, throughout the year the Antarctic remains much colder, partly due to the fact that most of the continent is high above sea level and is covered in thousands of metres of ice, rather than just a few metres as in the Arctic.

There are no native inhabitants on the Antarctic land mass, but special international treaties allow scientists from many countries to live there and undertake valuable research. Much of the information we know about the ozone layer and global warming has come from these scientists.

The following table provides a summary of some key facts about the polar regions of our planet.

	Arctic	Antarctic
Situation	Ocean surrounded by continents	Continent surrounded by oceans
Temperature in winter	–10°C to –30°C	–25°C to –70°C
Temperature in summer	0°C	–2°C to –40°C
Ice thickness	1.5 to 9 metres (floating sea ice)	2500 metres (average thickness)
Main animal life	Polar bears Whales Seals	Penguins Whales Seals
Human inhabitants	Inuits on the land surrounding the frozen ocean	Scientists from many countries

Polar Dream

Helen Thayer was born in New Zealand. She has become a world-famous adventurer, author and photographer, telling the stories of her adventures in words and pictures.

In 1988, at the age of 50, Helen decided to walk alone to the magnetic North Pole without the aid of aircraft, dog teams or snow mobiles. She was totally unsupported. She walked and skied, pulling her own 160 pound sled filled with all her supplies. Her only companion was Charlie, a black Canadian Eskimo Husky, who had been a valuable polar bear dog for the Inuit of Resolute Bay in the polar region of Northern Canada. Charlie's only job was to walk at Helen's side to protect her from polar bears. He did his job well. He saved her life at least once. They were confronted by seven polar bears, one at a time, throughout the almost month-long journey of 586 km (364 miles). Helen circumnavigated the entire magnetic North Pole area.

She began on 30 March and finished on 27 April. It was a long and lonely journey. Helen's expedition was the only one going to the magnetic North Pole in 1988, therefore she had no warning of the ice conditions which lay ahead of her.

She then wrote a book about her journey to the Pole titled *Polar Dream* with a foreword by Sir Edmund Hillary. It is the story of her faithful dog, Charlie, who travelled at her side during her journey. Charlie went home with Helen and lives with three other dogs, four goats and two donkeys. He runs daily with the Thayers, hikes and climbs mountains. He truly enjoys a life of luxury. As Helen will tell you, "What Charlie wants, Charlie gets."

Roald Amundsen

Roald Amundsen, a Norwegian, spent almost all his adult life in exploration. He was the first explorer to navigate the Northwest Passage between the Atlantic and the Pacific oceans to the north of Canada. However, he is most famous for being the first person to reach the South Pole. Yet his journey to Antarctica was almost an accident.

Amundsen was 37 years old when he decided in 1909 to make an attempt on the North Pole, which had not then been reached. But, while he was preparing for the journey, news came that the American explorer Robert Peary had arrived at the Pole. Amundsen secretly changed his plans, telling only his brother, and headed for the South Pole instead. He knew that a British expedition led by Robert Falcon Scott had already set out with the same aim, but travelling by a different route, he overtook the British party. Amundsen's five-man group set out from his base camp in October 1911 on sledges drawn by huskies on what was to be an eight-week journey. On 14 December 1911, Amundsen reached the Pole and planted the Norwegian flag there. He was about four weeks ahead of Scott.

Scott of the Antarctic

Scott of the Antarctic. Who was he?

Scott of the Antarctic is a nickname that has been given to the famous British naval officer and explorer Robert Falcon Scott. From a very early age, however, he was known as "Con" (from the name Falcon). Con joined the navy at the age of 13 and rose through the ranks over the next few years of his life. In late 1911 he led an expedition into unknown areas of Antarctica, aiming to become the first man to stand at the South Pole. On 17 January 1912, Scott reached his destination.

It's cold there. So what do you wear?

Modern polar explorers wear several layers of highly technical thermal, breathable and waterproof clothing. The fabrics used are lightweight and often very expensive. These clothes are used for sleeping too, when the explorer climbs into a specially made sleeping bag. Scott's party had none of this. They had to wear layer on layer of sweaters with woollen hats and woollen and fur mittens. Nature provided them with reindeer fur for boots and sleeping bags.

How on earth do you get to the South Pole?

With great difficulty. Even almost a hundred years later, explorers who attempt to make the South Pole on foot are often thwarted by dangerous conditions, even though they have lightweight equipment and sometimes use teams of dogs to help with the load. Imagine what it must have been like for Scott and his party. They did not have the luxury of a dog team and chose to pull their own supplies across the icy wastes of Antarctica.

So what did Scott find at the South Pole?

The following words were recorded in Scott's diary: "Great God! This is an awful place ..." Unfortunately for Scott it was not just the place itself that was awful. As his team approached the Pole they saw a speck in the distance. They got closer and realised the terrible truth – the speck was a Norwegian flag. Roald Amundsen had beaten them to the South Pole and the tracks of his dogs still lay in the snow. All Scott had to show for the journey were diary entries, photographs and 15 kilograms of fossils collected along the way.

What did Scott do next?

All he could do was turn around and lead his party back home. Luck was not on their side, however. They managed to get themselves just a few miles from relative safety but a huge blizzard and frost-bitten limbs prevented them going further. Scott wrote a final entry in his diary on 29 March, 1912 saying: "The end cannot be far." Somehow, although on the verge of death, he still managed to write letters to his loved ones. The bodies of the party were found eight months later.

Two o'clock:
Let out of the back door of the house, our cat
Is practising the snow.

The layer of white makes a small straight, crumbling cliff
Where we open the back door inwards. The cat
Sniffs at it with suspicion, learns you can just about
Pat at the flaking snow with a careful dab. Then,
A little bolder, he dints it with one whole foot
– And withdraws it, curls it as if slightly lame,

And looks down at it, oddly. The snow is
Different from anything else, not like
A rug, or a stretch of lino, or an armchair to claw upon
And be told to **Get off!**

The snow is peculiar, but not forbidden. The cat
Is welcome to go out in the snow. Does
The snow welcome the cat?
He thinks, looks, tries again.

Three paces out of the door, his white feet find
You sink a little way all of the time, it is slow and cold,
    but it
Doesn't particularly hurt. Perhaps you can even enjoy
    it as something new.
So he walks on, precisely, on the tips of very
    cautious paws …

Half past three, the cat stretched warm indoors,
From the bedroom window we can see his explorations

– From door to fence, from fence to gate, from gate to
    wall to tree, and back,
Are long patterned tracks and trade-routes of round
    paw-marks
Which fresh snow is quietly filling.

By Alan Brownjohn

Section 1

These questions are about the text "Polar Dream" on page 54.

Choose the correct word or group of words and put a ring around your choice.

1 Helen Thayer travelled to the magnetic North Pole by: *(1 mark)* ☐
                                                                               Q1

   aircraft.

   snow mobile.

   walking and skiing.

   car.

2 Charlie was a husky dog taken along on the journey to: *(1 mark)* ☐
                                                                               Q2

   pull the sled.

   scare away polar bears.

   enjoy the walk.

   be nice.

3 After the expedition Charlie: *(1 mark)* ☐
                                                                               Q3

   went back to the Inuits.

   hunted for polar bears.

   went to live with Helen.

   stayed in the Arctic.

subtotal

4   Helen took a sled along with her to: *(1 mark)*

sit on.

carry her supplies.

carry rocks she found.

shelter beneath.

5   Helen wrote a book about her journey called: *(1 mark)*

Polar Dream.

Travel with Charlie.

My Journey.

My Autobiography.

6   How did Charlie prove to be an invaluable companion on Helen Thayer's journey?
(1 mark)

_____

_____

7 Why does the text tell us that *"What Charlie wants, Charlie gets"*? (1 mark)

_____

_____

_____

8 List three things that made Helen's journey all the more remarkable. (2 marks)

a) _____

b) _____

c) _____

9 Sir Edmund Hillary was the first man to conquer Mount Everest. Why do you think the author mentions the fact that Sir Edmund Hillary wrote the foreword to Helen's book? (1 mark)

_____

_____

10 Why was Helen Thayer at a disadvantage as the only explorer to the magnetic North Pole that year? (1 mark)

_____

_____

_____

subtotal

Section 2

These questions are about the text "Roald Amundsen" on page 55.

11 What caused Amundsen to head for the South Pole? *(1 mark)*

Q11

_____

_____

_____

12 Why do you think Amundsen's plans were kept secret? *(1 mark)*

Q12

_____

_____

_____

13 Give two possible reasons why Amundsen chose a different
route to Scott. *(2 marks)*

Q13

_____

_____

_____

_____

14 Roald Amundsen's achievement was greater than that of Scott or Helen Thayer.

Do you agree with this opinion?
Explain your own opinion fully, using the texts to help you.

(3 marks)

_____

_____

_____

_____

_____

_____

Section 3

These questions are about the text "Scott of the Antarctic" on page 57.

15 Give two possible reasons, supported by information from the text,
for Scott taking longer than Amundsen to reach the Pole.   *(2 marks)*   Q15

a) _____

_____

_____

b) _____

_____

_____

16 What in the text indicates that Scott probably expected to die?   *(1 mark)*   Q16

_____

_____

17 Why do you think that Scott declared of the Pole,
"Great God! This is an awful place"?   *(2 marks)*   Q17

_____

_____

_____

_____

18 Several items are mentioned in the text about Captain Scott.
Match each item with its purpose.

(2 marks)

One has been done for you.

reindeer fur   evidence of expedition

diary   to transport supplies

fossils   to help with research

sledges   sleeping bags

photographs   to record thoughts and feelings

19 Page 57 is clearly divided into questions and answers.

How does this layout help the reader?

(1 mark)

_____

_____

_____

Section 4

These questions are about the poem "Explorer" by Alan Brownjohn on page 58.

20 What is the cat doing when it is "practising" the snow? *(1 mark)*

Q2

_____

_____

_____

21 In the third verse, the snow is described as *"different from anything else"*.
    What makes it different for the cat? *(2 marks)*

Q2

_____

_____

_____

_____

_____

22 Why does the author describe the snow as *"slow and cold"*? *(2 marks)*

Q2

_____

_____

_____

_____

23 *"From door to fence, from fence to gate, from gate to wall to tree, and back."*
Why do you think the poet divides this line into short sections
separated by commas?

(2 marks)

_____

_____

_____

_____

_____

24 Explain what the difference is between the snow in the garden at
two o'clock and the snow at half past three.

(2 marks)

_____

_____

_____

_____

subtotal

Section 5

These questions are about the whole of the Set B Reading Material.

25 Give two reasons why a trip to the South Pole during its winter
    would be more difficult.   *(2 marks)*

    a) _____

    _____

    b) _____

    _____

26 What purpose is served by the table at the end of the article "Pole to Pole"?

                                                          (1 mark)

    _____

    _____

27 Explain why you think that explorers such as Amundsen, Scott and Helen Thayer
    have always had a fascination with the North and South Poles.   *(3 marks)*

    _____

    _____

    _____

    _____

    _____

28 Making reference to the text, consider one advantage and two disadvantages of a trip to each pole as opposed to the other. *(3 marks)*

	Advantage	Disadvantage
North Pole	warmer climate	
South Pole		

29 Both texts *Roald Amundsen* and *Scott of the Antarctic* provide information about the race to be the first explorer to reach the South Pole in the early twentieth century.

Why do you think the following articles have been included? *(3 marks)*

"Pole to Pole"

_____

_____

_____

"Polar Dream"

_____

_____

_____

subtotal

"Explorer" poem

_____

_____

_____

30 What comparisons can be made between a polar explorer and the cat in the poem _Explorer_?

Explain your response, making reference to the text if this helps. *(3 marks)*

_____

_____

_____

_____

_____

_____

END OF TEST

TEST ADVICE

This information will not appear in a school test.
It is included here to remind you not to stop working
until you are told the 1 hour test is over.

Check your answers again if time.

DON'T JUST SIT THERE WHEN FINISHED

FINDING ONE MISTAKE CAN MEAN EXTRA MARKS.
IT MAY ONLY TAKE 1 MARK TO MOVE UP TO THE NEXT LEVEL.

DO YOUR BEST and DON'T PANIC.

Set
B

KEY STAGE 2
Levels 3–5

Long Writing
Test Paper

English

The 2-in-1 Super Coat

Long Writing Test Paper

The 2-in-1 Super Coat

Instructions:

- find a quiet place where you can sit down and complete the test paper undisturbed
- make sure you have all the necessary equipment to complete the test paper
- read the question carefully
- answer the question on lined paper
- go through and check your answer when you have finished writing

Time:

This test paper is **45 minutes long**. This includes planning and writing time. Aim to spend approximately **10 minutes** planning your writing using the planning prompts.

Check how your child has done against the Answers and Mark Scheme on pages 87–101.

	Max. Mark	**Actual Mark**
Score	31	....

First name ....

Last name ....

The 2-in-1 Super Coat

Some of your class have been asked to test the new *2-in-1 Super Coat* manufactured by a local company. The company need it testing by children before they produce their final version for sale in the shops.

The *2-in-1 Super Coat* has the following features.

1   Blue waterproof outer layer with a zip in/zip out fleece. The fleece and the outer layer can both be worn alone or together for extra warmth and waterproofing.

2   Suitable for both boys and girls.

3   Four large single button pockets on both layers.

4   A fixed hood on the outer layer.

5   Elasticated cuffs on both layers.

6   A special mobile phone pocket inside the fleece layer.

7   Reflective strips on the back of the outer layer.

8   Lightweight material for both layers.

9   A built-in safety light on the front of the outer layer.

Your task is to write a report about the jacket for the company. You should think about the features mentioned and say how these are good or poor design points. You can make recommendations to the company on how you feel the jacket could be changed before it goes on sale. Use the planning prompts to help you.

Planning

Use this page to make brief notes as you plan your ideas. These notes will not be marked.

Good features of the coat	Things that need to be improved

How will I start the report?

_____

_____

_____

How will I end the report?

_____

_____

_____

Set
B

KEY STAGE 2
Levels 3–5

Short Writing
Test Paper

English

Short Writing Test Paper

On Your Bike

Instructions:

- find a quiet place where you can sit down and complete the test paper undisturbed
- make sure you have all the necessary equipment to complete the test paper
- read the question carefully
- answer the question on lined paper
- go through and check your answer when you have finished writing

Time:

This test paper is **20 minutes** long. This includes planning and writing time. Aim to spend approximately **5 minutes** planning your writing using the planning prompts.

Check how your child has done against the Answers and Mark Scheme on pages 87–101.

	Max. Mark	**Actual Mark**
Score	12	....

First name

Last name

On Your Bike

Bicycle facts

1   Cycling is a very good form of exercise – ride a bike and keep fit.

2   Bicycles do not pollute the environment with nasty fumes.

3   Bicycles are quiet.

4   Bicycles are relatively safe if you wear a helmet and ride sensibly.

5   Cycling can be great fun.

The following letter has just been printed in your local newspaper:

Dear Editor,

I am fed up of the council building new cycle paths everywhere. I think bikes are a nuisance. Children are constantly riding up and down my street on their bikes and when I am driving I always end up having to overtake slow cyclists. Why can't the children walk and why can't grown-ups just use their cars?

I think bikes should be banned, leaving the streets for cars only. This will help everyone get to where they are going more quickly and make the world a safer place, because people will not fall off, or get knocked off, their bikes.

Yours sincerely,

Anne Eastwood

Your task is to write a letter to the newspaper persuading readers why you feel Anne Eastwood is wrong. Use the *Bicycle facts* and other information which you think should be included. Plan your work very briefly on the next page.

Planning

Make a few brief notes to help you plan your ideas. These notes will not be marked.

Points you will argue against	Evidence you will use

Set

B

KEY STAGE 2
Levels 3–5

Spelling
Test Paper

English

Cool Sports

Spelling Test Paper

Cool Sports

Instructions to parents:

- find a quiet place where you can sit down with your child
- make sure you have all the necessary equipment to complete the test paper
- read the short passage on page 102 to your child twice in its entirety
- during the first reading, your child should not write anything on the answer sheet
- during the second reading, pause after each word to be tested (shown in bold type), to enable your child to write the word in the gap on the answer sheet
- check how your child has done against the passage on page 102

	Max.	**Number of words correct**
Score	20	....

See page 103 for the spelling test mark conversion chart.

First name ....

Last name ....

Cool Sports

Despite being cold and hard, ice has become _____ used by

humans for many sports. They all _____ nerve and skill to both

maintain balance and _____ at the same time.

Ice-skating involves _____ yourself across ice using

_____ bladed boots _____ as skates. It is an

_____ popular sport throughout the world and has several forms.

Speed skating involves races on a frozen _____ over distances

of up to 10,000 _____. The races are much quicker than

_____ races on an athletics track. At the 1980 Winter Olympics,

the speed skater Eric Heiden won five gold medals, a _____

never previously _____ in the sport.

Figure skating is an event for individuals or mixed pairs. The

_____ skate to music while _____ to

perform a range of spectacular and _____ moves such as spins

and jumps. They are then _____ for technical merit, required

elements and _____.

Ice hockey is a team game _____ on ice. It is regarded as the

fastest team sport in the world with the players hitting the puck at well over 100 km

per hour. With the pace of the game and _____ crowds the

_____ often gets very exciting and sometimes violent.

Answers and Mark Scheme

Reading Test Papers

Set A Reading Test Paper "On Track"

Section 1: "The Green Dragon and the Old Gentleman"

1	the Green Dragon	*AF2 (1 mark)*
2	his hand	*AF2 (1 mark)*
3	wave to the Green Dragon	*AF2 (1 mark)*
4	take their love to father	*AF2 (1 mark)*
5	could be treated like a pet	*AF3 (1 mark)*

6 Award 1 mark for each of the following points (up to a maximum of 2 marks).
The trains made sounds like home/reminded them of the streets of London.   *AF3 (1 mark)*
They thought it might be going to where their father was.   *AF3 (1 mark)*

7 Award 2 marks for answers which make a comparison between the power/ferocity/awe of the train and that of a dragon and that it was as if/easy to imagine that the tunnel was the lair in which the dragon lived. Award 1 mark for answers which relate to the train or tunnel being like a dragon or its lair.   *AF5 (1–2 marks)*

8 Award 3 marks for fuller explanations which refer to the children thinking that the train is going to where their father is, their idea of sending their love to their father by the train and that they thought perhaps the old gentleman knew their father.
Award 2 marks for an explanation which includes two of the above points and award 1 mark for an explanation which includes just one of the above points.   *AF3 (1–3 marks)*

9 a) Award 1 mark for any reference to the use of handkerchiefs as a means of being more easily noticed.   *AF3 (1 mark)*
   b) Award 1 mark for reference to the fact that they were too excited or that they were children and the cleanliness of their handkerchiefs did not bother them.   *AF3 (1 mark)*

10 Award 1 mark for a brief explanation which suggests that Bobbie is looking after her siblings and reassures them.   *AF3 (1 mark)*

Section 2: "*The Railway Children* – From Book to Screen"

11 Award 1 mark for a brief explanation giving an overview of the fact that the section is about the book being made into a television programme/film.   *AF5 (1 mark)*

12 Award 1 mark for briefly explaining that the text shows that although it started life as a book it eventually found its way onto screen as a television programme and/or films.   *AF6 (1 mark)*

13 Award 1 mark (up to maximum of 2 marks) for inclusion of any of the following.
Members of the Royal Family were guests at the premiere.
At Christmas 1970 it was shown privately to the Queen and other members of the Royal Family.
It was voted among the best one hundred British Pictures of the past century.
It is included in the Chicago Museum of Fine Arts.   *AF2 (1–2 marks)*

Section 3: "An Interview With the Railway Children"

14 Award 2 marks for a fuller explanation of the feeling that modern-day children grow up more quickly compared to children in the past. Award 1 mark for a simple response stating that children today are treated as young adults from an earlier age (without comparison to the past).   *AF7 (1–2 marks)*

15 Award 1 mark for a reference to the fact that they were dressed in Edwardian costume.   *AF3 (1 mark)*

16 Award 1 mark for reference to the restricted movement, feeling like a doll or feeling younger.   *AF2 (1 mark)*

Section 4: "A Small World"

17 Award 3 marks for fuller explanations which refer to the increased speed and convenience of travel when the railways came along. There should also be reference to this speed and convenience making distant places more easily accessible, thus making it seem like the world is now smaller. Award 2 marks for reference to increased speed, convenience and accessibility but no reference to a shrinking world. Award 1 mark for a simple reference to any of speed, convenience or accessibility.

AF7 (1–3 marks)

18 Award 2 marks for the correct order of: (1) Trevithick tests the first steam locomotive (given); (2) The Rocket wins the Rainhill Trials; (3) The Mallard sets the world record; (4) The Japanese Bullet train makes its first journey.
Award 1 mark for one event in the correct place (in addition to that given).

AF2 (1–2 marks)

19 Award 1 mark for reference to the use of new technology/diesel trains/ electric trains.

AF3 (1 mark)

20 Award 2 marks for an explanation that the timeline provides a visual aid to support the text and that it enables other events/facts to be easily placed alongside information already given.
Award 1 mark for a reference to either of the above points.

AF4 (1–2 marks)

21 Award 1 mark for a brief explanation that these passages have been used to show the advance in trains from the early days to modern high speed trains.

AF4 (1 marks)

Section 5: "Travelling in Style"

22 Award 2 marks for all the correct pairings of: fine views – through the windows (given); a piano – in the bar; wood panelling – in the compartments; finest crystal glasses – in the dining car.
Award 1 mark for one correct pairing (in addition to that given)

AF2 (1–2 marks)

23 2 marks for an explanation that the train is long and "snake-like", and that its journey will be a winding one. Award 1 mark for reference to either of the above points.

AF5 (1–2 marks)

24 Award 2 marks for correctly identifying: wealthy, luxury, rich, romantic.
Award 1 mark for correct identification of 2 or 3 of these words.

AF5 (1–2 marks)

25 Award 1 mark for reference to a personal steward.

AF3 (1 mark)

Section 6: The whole of the Set A Reading Material

26 Award 2 marks for a response of "yes" or "no" with a full explanation of the reason. E.g. Yes because trains are big and fast and you can see different things from them. Trains are exciting because most of the time people go to places in cars. OR No, because we have cars and aeroplanes now and people don't need to use trains as much. Children have many more technologies to be excited about.
Award 1 mark for explanations which cover only single points.

AF7 (1–2 marks)

27 Award 2 marks for an explanation which refers to the inclusion of the article to show that rail travel is still seen as glamorous by some people and that there can be more to rail travel than simply getting from one place to another.
Award 1 mark for an explanation which refers to just one of the above points.

AF6 (1–2 marks)

28 Award 2 marks for reference to the fact that trains run on railway tracks and/or that the content of the Reading Material is about trains and (by default) railway tracks. Award 1 mark for a single point.

AF6 (1–2 marks)

29 Award 2 marks for an explanation which refers to such a website existing, so people can find further information about *The Railway Children* and to serve as a focal point for fans of the book, the film and trains.
Award 1 mark for reference to one of the above points.

AF3 (1–2 marks)

30 Award 3 marks for a fuller explanation which refers to the use of fiction and non-fiction elements to indicate the development of rail travel, the early fascination with trains and railways (particularly illustrated by the extract from the book) and modern-day interest (particularly illustrated by the "From Book to Screen" article and the "Travelling in Style" article). Reference should be made to sections of the text in the response. Award 2 marks for an explanation which does not cover all of the above points but does refer to some of the sections of text. Award 1 mark for an explanation which covers any of the above points without reference to the sections of text.

AF6

(1–3 marks)

The following table shows the breakdown of marks for each Assessment Focus in the Reading Test for Set A. Using the Mark Schemes, total the number of marks your child has scored against each Assessment Focus. This will provide you with a good idea of areas of strength and areas for development in their comprehension skills. Enter the total score on the marking grid on page 8.

	Max Score	Score
AF2	11	
AF3	14	
AF4	3	
AF5	7	
AF6	8	
AF7	7	

Set B Reading Test Paper "Polar Explorer"

Section 1: "Polar Dream"

1 walking and skiing   *AF2 (1 mark)*

2 scare away polar bears   *AF2 (1 mark)*

3 went to live with Helen   *AF2 (1 mark)*

4 carry her supplies   *AF3 (1 mark)*

5 Polar Dream   *AF2 (1 mark)*

6 Award 1 mark for any reference to the fact that Charlie saved her life when confronted by polar bears.   *AF3 (1 mark)*

7 Award 1 mark for an explanation that Helen values Charlie for saving her life/scaring away polar bears.   *AF3 (1 mark)*

8 Award 2 marks for inclusion of three, or 1 mark for inclusion of two of the following: she was unsupported, she pulled her own sled, she was on foot, she had no warning of ice conditions.   *AF2 (1–2 marks)*

9 Award 1 mark for an explanation that this shows that another famous explorer considered Helen's achievement to be remarkable.   *AF6 (1 mark)*

10 Award 1 mark for reference to the fact that as the only expedition that year she had no warning of the ice conditions.   *AF3 (1 mark)*

Section 2: "Roald Amundsen"

11 Award 1 mark for a brief explanation that he had been beaten to the North Pole, his original destination.   *AF3 (1 mark)*

12 Award 1 mark for a brief explanation that Amundsen did not want to alert Scott to his intention to beat him to the South Pole.   *AF3 (1 mark)*

13 Award 1 mark (up to a maximum of 2) for each reason given from: he did not want to be seen by Scott; he had a better route/faster route.   *AF3 (1–2 marks)*

14 Award 3 marks for a response of "yes" or "no" with a fully explained reason making use of at least two well-elaborated points. Award 2 marks for at least two well explained points without as much elaboration. Award 1 mark for a single point with some explanation or two or more points without any explanation.   *AF7 (1–3 marks)*

Section 3: "Scott of the Antarctic"

15 Award 1 mark for each reason given from: they had no dogs to pull their sledges (or they had to pull their own sledges); they were slowed down by the extra weight of fossils they had collected.   *AF3 (1–2 marks)*

16 Award 1 mark for reference to Scott's final diary entry.   *AF3 (1 mark)*

17 Award 2 marks for an explanation which includes reference to the cold/icy conditions at the Pole and reference to Scott's disappointment at arriving after Amundsen. Award 1 mark for reference to just one of the above points.   *AF3 (1–2 marks)*

18 Award 2 marks for all the correct pairings of: reindeer fur – sleeping bags (given); sledges – to transport supplies; diary – to record thoughts and feelings; fossils – to help with research; photographs – evidence of expedition. Award 1 mark for two correct pairings (in addition to that given).   *AF3 (1–2 marks)*

19 Award 1 mark for an explanation that the questions and answers help the reader to locate information with greater ease and/or help the text to focus on important information.   *AF4 (1 mark)*

Section 4: "Explorer"

20 Award 1 mark for any indication that the cat is feeling what the snow is like. *AF3 (1 mark)*

21 Award 2 marks for a fuller explanation which makes reference to the cat being allowed to play on the snow without being told to "get off". There should also be an indication that the snow is unfamiliar and the cat can feel how cold the snow is. Award 1 mark for the first explanation only. *AF3 (1–2 marks)*

22 Award 2 marks for a response which refers to the fact that snow is very cold and that because the cat's paws would sink into the snow a little, either this made the progress slow or the progress is slowed because the cat tests the snow. Award 1 mark for only one of the above. *AF5 (1–2 marks)*

23 Award 2 marks for an explanation that this style breaks down the cat's movements into sections and matches the cat's stop-start movements as it explores the snow. Award 1 mark for an explanation which only covers one of the above points. *AF4 (1–2 marks)*

24 Award 2 marks for an explanation which makes a contrast between the fresh, probably untouched snow at the start of the poem and the snow covered with the paw marks of the cat at the end of the poem. Award 1 mark for a brief response that the snow now has paw marks/tracks across it. *AF3 (1–2 marks)*

Section 5: The whole of the Set B Reading Material

25 Award 1 mark for each of the following responses with or without explanation: it is darker (because the sun stays below the horizon in the Antarctic winter); it is colder. *AF3 (1–2 marks)*

26 Award 1 mark for an explanation that the table summarises information and/or that it makes it easier for the reader to view basic facts. *AF4 (1 mark)*

27 Award 3 marks for a fuller explanation which includes at least three of the following points: some people find it exciting/fascinating to put themselves in danger/to push themselves to their limits; it is a challenging place to go to because of the very cold temperatures and the dangers from the weather and animals; it is an exciting place because of the danger; they are very beautiful places because of the snow and the interesting wildlife; it is fascinating because these places are largely untouched by humans. Award 2 marks for a response which includes two of the points and award 1 mark for a response which includes just one point. *AF7 (1–3 marks)*

28 Award 1 mark for each correct selection from the choices below:

	Advantage	Disadvantage
North Pole	warmer climate (given)	the ice is floating; the ice is moving; the ice could melt in summer; thinner ice could crack; dark winters; polar bears
South Pole	there are bases there; it's on land; the ice isn't moving; the ice is very thick and won't crack; no polar bears	very cold all year round; dark winters; altitude makes it more difficult

AF3 (1–3 marks)

29 Award 1 mark for a correct explanation for each part of the Reading Material.
   "Pole to Pole"   to provide background information about the polar regions/to demonstrate the challenging environments the polar regions represent.

"Polar Dream"   to show that female explorers are capable of meeting the most demanding challenges/to show that polar exploration is still very demanding and challenging even though the poles were first reached during the last century.

"Explorer" poem to put the term "exploration" into a more familiar context/to show that exploration does not just mean going to extreme places.   *AF6*

(1–3 marks)

30 Award 3 marks for a fuller explanation that makes reference to the text and includes at least three of the following points: a polar explorer having to rise to the challenge in a similar way to the cat taking its first steps in the snow; the polar regions are different from anywhere else on Earth, just as the snow is different for the cat; movement is cautious for the cat, just as it must be for a polar explorer and the snow is "slow and cold" for both the cat and a polar explorer; both the cat and the polar explorer leave tracks in the snow. Award 2 marks for a response which makes two of the above points. Award 1 mark for a response which makes very simple points without comparison or elaboration.   *AF3*

(1–3 marks)

The following table shows the breakdown of marks for each Assessment Focus in the Reading Test for Set B. Using the Mark Schemes, total the number of marks your child has scored against each Assessment Focus. This will provide you with a good idea of the areas of strength and areas for development in their comprehension skills. Enter the total score on the marking grid on page 8.

	Max Score	Score
AF2	6	
AF3	28	
AF4	4	
AF5	2	
AF6	4	
AF7	6	

Writing Test Papers

The Writing Test Paper is marked out of 50. The total score is found by adding together the scores for the Long and Short Writing Tests and the Spelling Test. The Long and Short Writing Tests are covered by six Mark Strands (A to F). Using the mark scheme and samples on the following pages, you should be able to apply a score to each Strand. Enter each Strand's score into the marking grid on page 8.

Set A and B Long Writing Test
Strand A – sentence structure and punctuation

Set A Yes No	Set B Yes No	*How well have you used sentences and punctuation?*
☐ ☐	☐ ☐	Are many of your ideas and sentences very simple or linked by "and/so" or "then"?
☐ ☐	☐ ☐	Do you use capital letters and full stops for some sentences?

Award 1 mark if this is the best description of your writing.

Set A Yes No	Set B Yes No	
☐ ☐	☐ ☐	Do your sentences have a correct basic grammatical structure (e.g. do subjects and verbs agree)?
☐ ☐	☐ ☐	Have you used simple joining words such as "and/but/or/because"?
☐ ☐	☐ ☐	Have you used simple descriptive phrases (e.g. "a big door", "she walked slowly")?
☐ ☐	☐ ☐	Are most of your sentences punctuated correctly with full stops and capital letters, and have you used commas in lists?

Award 2 marks if your writing matches most of this description.
Award 3 marks if your writing matches all of this description.

Set A Yes No	Set B Yes No	
☐ ☐	☐ ☐	Do you have some variety of sentence structures (e.g. longer sentences, shorter sentences, statements, instructions) with good use of nouns, verbs and adjectives to elaborate your ideas?
☐ ☐	☐ ☐	Have you used some complex sentences (e.g. clauses linked by "so that", "although", "which")?
☐ ☐	☐ ☐	Are your tenses and pronouns consistent?
☐ ☐	☐ ☐	Have you used descriptive phrases (e.g. "an eerie silence", "hidden behind the zip")?
☐ ☐	☐ ☐	Have you used capital letters, full stops, question marks and exclamation marks correctly in most cases?
☐ ☐	☐ ☐	Have you used punctuation within sentences (e.g. commas, apostrophes, speech marks)?

Award 4 marks if your writing matches most of this description.
Award 5 marks if your writing matches all of this description.

Set A Yes No	Set B Yes No	
☐ ☐	☐ ☐	Are your sentences varied in length and structure?
☐ ☐	☐ ☐	Have you used descriptive phrases and/or subordinate clauses to build up detail and interest?
☐ ☐	☐ ☐	Are your sentences (including complex sentences) mostly grammatically correct?
☐ ☐	☐ ☐	Have you used a variety of connectives?
☐ ☐	☐ ☐	Have you correctly used capital letters, full stops, question marks and exclamation marks in almost all cases?
☐ ☐	☐ ☐	Have you used punctuation within sentences (dashes, brackets, colons, including the punctuation of speech) and is this used correctly in most cases?

Award 6 marks if your writing matches most of this description.
Award 7 marks if your writing matches all of this description.

Set A Yes No	Set B Yes No	
☐ ☐	☐ ☐	Have you effectively used a wide range of structures to give your writing impact? Does the use of appropriate phrasing and sentencing allow the writing to convey subtle shades of meaning?
☐ ☐	☐ ☐	Is a wide range of punctuation used as appropriate to the structure of the sentences?
☐ ☐	☐ ☐	Is all punctuation accurate?

Award 8 marks if your writing matches all of this description.

Maximum marks for this Strand: 8.

Set A and B Long Writing Test
Strand B – text structure and organisation

Set A Set B
Yes No Yes No   *How effectively have you structured and organised your writing?*

☐ ☐ ☐ ☐ Does your writing rely on simple connectives to show the relationship between events (e.g. "one day", "and/then", "suddenly…")?

☐ ☐ ☐ ☐ Have you sequenced the events in a sensible order?

Award 1 mark if this is the best description of your writing.

☐ ☐ ☐ ☐ Is there some indication that your ideas have been organised (e.g. some grouping of ideas or sentences; beginning or end section may be a separate paragraph)?

☐ ☐ ☐ ☐ Do you have a simple but coherent relationship between ideas (e.g. time markers such as "before", "as soon as", "an hour later")?

☐ ☐ ☐ ☐ Do you maintain simple links to avoid confusion (e.g. clear use of pronouns such as "I", "she", "they")?

Award 2 marks if your writing matches most of this description.
Award 3 marks if your writing matches all of this description.

☐ ☐ ☐ ☐ Does your writing have a suitable opening?

☐ ☐ ☐ ☐ Does your writing have clearly defined beginning, middle and end sections?

☐ ☐ ☐ ☐ Are the events in your writing logically organised (e.g. chronologically)?

☐ ☐ ☐ ☐ Have you signalled time/space relationships between events (e.g. "during the following afternoon", "to the left of the spacious pocket")?

☐ ☐ ☐ ☐ Are your sentences grouped to distinguish, e.g. action, description or dialogue?

☐ ☐ ☐ ☐ Have you used paragraphs to mark the beginning, main events and ending?

☐ ☐ ☐ ☐ Have you used details of setting/context to develop the plot or ideas?

Award 4 marks if your writing matches most of this description.
Award 5 marks if your writing matches all of this description.

☐ ☐ ☐ ☐ Is your writing well organised and convincingly structured?

☐ ☐ ☐ ☐ Have you achieved controlled and interesting movement through the text (e.g. flashback, reference to events that follow)?

☐ ☐ ☐ ☐ Does your writing have variety in the relationships between ideas (e.g. contrasts in mood or pacing)?

☐ ☐ ☐ ☐ Are these relationships between ideas signalled in a variety of ways (e.g. a variety of connectives, adverbial phrases)?

☐ ☐ ☐ ☐ Does the relationship between the paragraphs add to the cohesiveness of your text?

☐ ☐ ☐ ☐ Have you used paragraphs confidently?

Award 6 marks if your writing matches most of this description.
Award 7 marks if your writing matches all of this description.

☐ ☐ ☐ ☐ Has your text been organised to achieve a particular effect?

☐ ☐ ☐ ☐ Is your story line or idea well developed so that complications are convincingly resolved?

☐ ☐ ☐ ☐ Are the various elements of your text drawn together to make a convincing conclusion?

☐ ☐ ☐ ☐ Do you have a variety in the length and structure of individual paragraphs which add to the overall effect of your text?

Award 8 marks if your writing matches all of this description.

Maximum marks for this Strand: 8.

Set A Long Writing Test "A Peculiar Incident"
Strand C – composition and effect

How effectively have you told the story?

Yes No

☐ ☐ Does your writing attempt to tell a story?

☐ ☐ Does your writing have the elements of a simple story, i.e. two or more related events; one or more characters?

☐ ☐ Have you made some attempt to interest the reader?

Award 1 mark if your writing matches most of this description.
Award 2 marks if your writing matches all of this description.

☐ ☐ Does your writing attempt to tell a story related to the starting point?

☐ ☐ Do you have a beginning and a sequence of events?

☐ ☐ Have you made an attempt to distinguish between characters (e.g. through what they say or do)?

☐ ☐ Have you included some details designed to create interest, humour or suspense?

☐ ☐ Does your story have a simple ending?

Award 3 mark if your writing matches some of this description.
Award 4 mark if your writing matches most of this description.
Award 5 marks if your writing matches all of this description.

☐ ☐ Is your story reasonably well paced?

☐ ☐ Does the ending relate to the main plot?

☐ ☐ Is there significant interaction between your characters (e.g. through dialogue)?

☐ ☐ Is there some development of your characters through what they say or do?

☐ ☐ Have you included details to help the reader (e.g. about the setting of the story or the characters)?

Award 6 marks if your writing matches some of this description.
Award 7 marks if your writing matches most of this description.
Award 8 marks if your writing matches all of this description.

☐ ☐ Have you used interesting story devices, e.g. does it start with dialogue or in the middle of a dramatic event? Does it include a sub-plot or a "twist"?

☐ ☐ Is your ending convincing?

☐ ☐ Have you engaged and kept the reader's interest (e.g. through suspense, lively characterisation, comments on events)?

☐ ☐ Are your events, description and dialogue suitably interwoven?

☐ ☐ Is Standard English used, or colloquialism or dialect used only for effect (e.g. in dialogue)?

☐ ☐ Is your writing a convincing story type (e.g. mystery, traditional tale)?

Award 9 marks if your writing matches some of this description.
Award 10 marks if your writing matches most of this description.
Award 11 marks if your writing matches all of this description.

☐ ☐ Does your story engage and keep the reader's interest throughout?

☐ ☐ Do you draw the reader into the story through the use of various devices (e.g. imagery, metaphor and simile)?

☐ ☐ Does your story have a theme (controlling idea) as well as a convincing plot?

☐ ☐ Is there an interplay between characters and events?

☐ ☐ Do your characters develop or change as a result of the story (e.g. by facing conflict or solving problems)?

☐ ☐ Are characters given substance according to their importance to the theme or plot?

☐ ☐ Have you drawn all elements together to make a satisfying conclusion?

Award 12 marks if your writing matches all of this description.

Maximum marks for this Strand: 12.

Set B Long Writing Test "The 2-in-1 Super Coat"
Strand C – composition and effect

How effectively have you written the report?

Yes No

☐ ☐	Does your writing attempt to report about the product?
☐ ☐	Does your writing have the elements of a simple report, i.e. basic information about one or more key points?
☐ ☐	Have you made some attempt to interest the reader?

Award 1 mark if your writing matches most of this description.
Award 2 marks if your writing matches all of this description.

☐ ☐	Have you attempted to relate your report to the starting point?
☐ ☐	Do you have a beginning and a sequence of points?
☐ ☐	Have you made an attempt to distinguish between different features?
☐ ☐	Have you included some details designed to create interest?
☐ ☐	Does your report have a simple ending?

Award 3 marks if your writing matches some of this description.
Award 4 marks if your writing matches most of this description.
Award 5 marks if your writing matches all of this description.

☐ ☐	Is your report reasonably well paced?
☐ ☐	Does the ending relate to the rest of the report?
☐ ☐	Have you made links between various points?
☐ ☐	Is there some development of the points you make (e.g. reasons)?
☐ ☐	Have you included details to help the reader (e.g. about the background to the report or by comparison with familiar items)?

Award 6 marks if your writing matches some of this description.
Award 7 marks if your writing matches most of this description.
Award 8 marks if your writing matches all of this description.

☐ ☐	Have you used devices such as description, evaluation and justification?
☐ ☐	Is your ending convincing?
☐ ☐	Have you engaged and kept the reader's interest (e.g. through interesting points, lively commentary)?
☐ ☐	Are your ideas, opinions and evidence suitably interwoven?
☐ ☐	Have you included positive points and suggestions for improvement?

Award 9 marks if your writing matches some of this description.
Award 10 marks if your writing matches most of this description.
Award 11 marks if your writing matches all of this description.

☐ ☐	Does your report engage and keep the reader's interest throughout?
☐ ☐	Do you draw the reader into the report through the use of various devices (e.g. imagery, metaphor and simile)?
☐ ☐	Have you commented on the product from differing points of view (e.g. "I would use this feature although others may find it frustrating …")?
☐ ☐	Are all of your points elaborated and justified in your writing?
☐ ☐	Have you written an effective conclusion which summarises the report and/or makes a direct appeal to the reader?

Award 12 marks if your writing matches all of this description.

Maximum marks for this Strand: 12.

Set A and B Short Writing Test
Strand D – sentence structure, punctuation and text organisation

Set A	Set B	
Yes No	Yes No	*How well have you organised your writing and used grammar and punctuation?*
☐ ☐	☐ ☐	Are many of your ideas and sentences very simple or linked by "and/so" or "then"?
☐ ☐	☐ ☐	Is there some connection between your sentences (e.g. pronouns such as "he" or "it" referring back to objects or participants already encountered)?
☐ ☐	☐ ☐	Do you use capital letters and full stops for some sentences?

Award 1 mark if this is the best description of your writing.

Set A	Set B	
☐ ☐	☐ ☐	Have you used simple adjectives (e.g. "it was fun", "I liked it")?
☐ ☐	☐ ☐	Have you made an attempt to organise the information into different areas?
☐ ☐	☐ ☐	Do your sentences have a correct basic grammatical structure (e.g. do subjects and verbs agree)?
☐ ☐	☐ ☐	Have you used simple joining words such as "and/but/or/if"?
☐ ☐	☐ ☐	Do you use simple statements and simple instruction forms (e.g. "he has a clown's nose", "don't drive so fast")?
☐ ☐	☐ ☐	Are most of your sentences punctuated correctly with full stops and capital letters, and have you used commas in lists?

Award 2 marks if this is the best description of your writing.

Set A	Set B	
☐ ☐	☐ ☐	Is your information mainly organised into suitable sections?
☐ ☐	☐ ☐	Do you have some variety of sentence structures (e.g. longer sentences, shorter sentences, statements, instructions) with good use of nouns, verbs and adjectives to elaborate your ideas?
☐ ☐	☐ ☐	Are your tenses and pronouns consistent?
☐ ☐	☐ ☐	Have you used capital letters, full stops, question marks and exclamation marks correctly in most cases?
☐ ☐	☐ ☐	Have you used punctuation within sentences (e.g. commas, apostrophes)?

Award 3 marks if this is the best description of your writing.

Set A	Set B	
☐ ☐	☐ ☐	Are the sections of your writing developed around the main themes of the topic?
☐ ☐	☐ ☐	Is similar content grouped together (e.g. in paragraphs or under headings)?
☐ ☐	☐ ☐	Are your sentences varied in length and structure?
☐ ☐	☐ ☐	Have you used a variety of connectives?
☐ ☐	☐ ☐	Are almost all of your sentences grammatically correct?
☐ ☐	☐ ☐	Have you used a range of punctuation in your writing (including punctuation within sentences) and has it almost always been used correctly?

Award 4 marks if this is the best description of your writing.

Maximum marks for this Strand: 4.

Set A and B Short Writing Test
Strand E – composition and effect

Set A   Set B   *How effectively have you written the shorter task?*
Yes No Yes No

☐☐ ☐☐   Does your writing attempt to give information?

☐☐ ☐☐   Does your writing include some statements or instructions, but assumes that the reader already knows the background?

Award 1 mark if this is the best description of your writing.

☐☐ ☐☐   Does your writing attempt to give information related to the starting point?

☐☐ ☐☐   Have you clearly separated individual statements or instructions from each other (e.g. starting on a new line)?

☐☐ ☐☐   Have you included some details designed to give a clear picture or create interest for the reader (e.g. 'It has a long, twisting slide', 'Cars sit bumper to bumper')?

☐☐ ☐☐   Does your writing show some understanding of what readers need to know?

Award 2 marks if your writing matches most of this description.
Award 3 marks if your writing matches all of this description.

☐☐ ☐☐   Have you addressed the reader directly (e.g. 'You will really enjoy it')?

☐☐ ☐☐   Does your writing give a fairly clear picture of the subject and the circumstances (e.g. 'the train is for children everywhere', 'cycling is more convenient in traffic')?

☐☐ ☐☐   Does your writing give an appropriate amount of information (i.e. not too little or too much)?

☐☐ ☐☐   Are descriptive phrases used for detail and clarity to help the reader (e.g. 'each brightly coloured carriage has a different activity')?

☐☐ ☐☐   Have you attempted to give the reader significant and helpful details (e.g. 'You can use the Fun-tastic Express at a nearby major town or city', 'Bicycles do not cause pollution of the environment')?

☐☐ ☐☐   Are the points you make sequenced appropriately?

Award 4 marks if your writing matches most of this description.
Award 5 marks if your writing matches all of this description.

☐☐ ☐☐   Have you engaged the reader's interest directly (e.g. through lively imaginative touches, a convincing picture of the situation)?

☐☐ ☐☐   Have you included additional details to increase the reader's understanding and/or enjoyment of the writing?

☐☐ ☐☐   Do you have a suitable balance between conciseness and detail (i.e. good detail but used precisely to make or elaborate a point)?

☐☐ ☐☐   Is the tone of your writing consistent (e.g. friendly/firm but clear)?

☐☐ ☐☐   Does your writing conform to the conventions of the type of text you have been asked to write (e.g. a persuasive letter)?

☐☐ ☐☐   Is your writing set out appropriately (e.g. using headings or paragraphs with relevant information grouped into these sections)?

Award 6 marks if your writing matches most of this description.
Award 7 marks if your writing matches all of this description.

☐☐ ☐☐   Does your writing engage and keep the reader's interest throughout?

☐☐ ☐☐   Does your writing read like a text in the style required by the task?

☐☐ ☐☐   Have you adapted and shaped the content of your writing for effect?

Award 8 marks if your writing matches all of this description.

Maximum marks for this Strand: 8

Handwriting

Set A and B Long Writing Test
Strand F – Handwriting

Handwriting is assessed for legibility and fluency in the Long Writing Test. You should judge the legibility and the clarity of the handwriting throughout the piece. Additionally, you should decide whether letters are correctly formed and have an appropriate size. The Mark Scheme Bands for handwriting are given below along with handwriting examples.

Set A Yes No	Set B Yes No	*How neatly have you written during the longer task?*
☐ ☐	☐ ☐	Is your handwriting legible?
☐ ☐	☐ ☐	Are most of your letters of similar size (e.g. h, k, l and g, p, y) and the correct size?
☐ ☐	☐ ☐	Is your spacing between most letters regular?

Award 1 mark if this is the best description of your handwriting.

Band F1 example: *It's great to play on bikes daily*

☐ ☐	☐ ☐	Are your letters the right size most of the time?
☐ ☐	☐ ☐	Is your writing joined most of the time?
☐ ☐	☐ ☐	Have you used appropriate spacing between words and letters?

Award 2 marks if this is the best description of your handwriting.

Band F2 example: *It's great to play on bikes daily.*

☐ ☐	☐ ☐	Is your writing joined and legible throughout the text?
☐ ☐	☐ ☐	Is your joined writing fluent (i.e. do the letter joins seem to "flow" evenly)?
☐ ☐	☐ ☐	Is the space between your letters and words even?
☐ ☐	☐ ☐	Are you developing a personal style in handwriting?

Award 3 marks if this is the best description of your handwriting.

Band F3 example: *It's great to play on bikes daily.*

Maximum marks for this Strand: 3.

Sample Marking of the Set A Long Writing Test – "A Peculiar Incident"

Strand A – sentence structure and punctuation
How well have you used sentences and punctuation?

This writing has a variety of long and short sentences with a range of structures including complex sentences (e.g. ... *I remembered the screams and people jumping into the water ...*). The writer uses descriptive phrases (e.g. ... *floating in a large white rowing boat in the middle of the ocean ...*) to build detail and add interest. The sentences are grammatically correct, and use connectives and a range of punctuation correctly (including punctuation within sentences). A wider range of connectives and a demonstration of knowledge of the use of more punctuation marks would help this writing to achieve a higher mark than the 6 marks it merits.

(6 marks)

Strand B – text structure and organisation
How effectively have you structured and organised your writing?

The writing is well organised and has a convincing structure with strong beginning, middle and end sections. The flow of the story is well controlled and the writer takes the characters from one setting to another very effectively. There is good variety in the relationships between ideas and these are demonstrated through changes in pace (floating on the sea followed by the storm) and mood (fear of the situation followed by the sombre memories of the cries and the bodies). The relationship between the confidently used paragraphs helps to make this a very cohesive piece of writing. Greater use of connectives and adverbial phrases would enhance the writing and take it beyond the 6 marks it merits.

(6 marks)

Strand C – composition and effect
How effectively have you written the story?

This story has an interesting "peculiar incident" with the characters taken back in time. This is then cleverly explained by the twist in the effective ending. Good description of events and an element of suspense keep the reader's interest throughout and all features of the story are suitably interwoven (e.g. use of speech to tell the reader about events). Greater characterisation, a demonstration of the use of devices such as simile and metaphor, and reference to the personal emotions of the narrator would improve the writing, which merits 9 marks.

(9 marks awarded)

Strand F – handwriting
How neatly have you written during the longer task?

The majority of the letters are the correct size, and there is consistency in the spacing of words. This handwriting receives 2 marks despite the writer having developed a personal style.

Varied sentence structure.

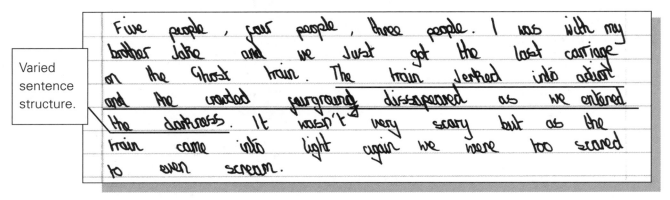

There were no other carriages and no other people. We were floating in a <u>large white rowing boat</u> in the middle of the ocean.

Descriptive phrase.

"Titanic", whispered Jake his eyes full of fear "Titanic", he repeated more slowly.

"Don't be so ridicu..." I stopped as I read a sign on the wooden seat opposite me. I remembered the screams and people jumping into the water. I remembered the bodies and cries just like in the film. Then I remembered the <u>titanic</u> sinking into the icey water.

Capitalisation of proper noun not used.

Now it was daylight and we sat in the life boat. The wind was getting stronger <u>and</u> we were getting colder. We shouted for help but it was no use ... The waves got bigger <u>and</u> bigger. Suddenly a big wave came onto us. I closed my eyes and I heard a bang as our boat snapped in two.

Simple connectives.

Clear, main event.

I opened my eyes and heard another bang as our carriage bumped into the one in front. We were back at the fairground, we got off the ride and walked to mum and dad. "Look at you two". Soaked wet through. "Was that fun?" questioned dad. Neither of us answered "<u>Too scared to talk then?</u>" he laughed.

Confident use of paragraphs.

Colloquial phrasing.

When we got home we sat in front of the television and watched a programme about the titanic. "Your great grandad and his sister were on the titanic you know it would have been his birthday this week, he used to work rides at a fairground." Nobody knew if they got to a lifeboat or not".

Explanatory twist in effective ending.

Nobody knew except me and my brother.

Sample Marking of the Set A Short Writing Test – "Fun-tastic Express"

Strand D – sentence structure, punctuation and text organisation
How well have you organised your writing and used grammar and punctuation?

This writing develops the theme coherently and the content is well organised into distinct paragraphs. A variety of sentence structure and length has been used and devices to connect parts of sentences have been used creatively (e.g. ...*With tunnels and loops, this has to be the best ride ever*). The sentences are mostly grammatically correct, and a range of punctuation has been used correctly and to good effect. This writing merits 4 marks.　　　　　　　　　　　　　　　*(4 marks)*

Strand E – composition and effect
How effectively have you written the shorter task?

The reader is immediately alerted to the fact that this writing is about something special (*Thrilling, fast, exciting and fun!*) The writing addresses the reader directly and the pace adds to the general feeling that the writer is very enthusiastic about the train. There is a balance between conciseness and detail (greater detail about the rollercoaster, less detail about the other attractions) and, apart from a repetition of the list of attractions, there is no unnecessary information. There is a consistently friendly tone and the writing certainly conforms to the conventions of an informative piece.
The effect is enhanced by clear paragraphing of grouped information which provides a smooth flow to the writing. A little more information about the rollercoaster (the favourite activity) would add to the overall effect and for this reason this writing merits 6 rather than 7 marks.　　　　*(6 marks)*

Thrilling, fast, exciting and fun! Come to the fun-tastic Express to have the best time ever on a train. You'll never believe that there is a magician, an adventure playground, a ball pool and a mini-rollercoaster on the train at your train station.

My favourite ride was the mini-rollercoaster. The rollercoaster comes in and out of the train in a mad kind of way. With tunnels and loops, this has to be the best ride ever. All the rides are brilliant, the ball pool and magician to chill out, and an adventure playground to test your strength.

You must go to this fun and exciting train. Even if you can't go on a trip on the train, why not spare a morning here? Its more fun going on the train than just reading about it. Why not come and have the time of your life?

For your free information pack, visit your local train station now!

Comma in list of objectives.

Added detail draws reader in.

Friendly tone.

Sample Marking of the Set B Long Writing Test – "The 2-in-1 Super Coat"

Strand A – sentence structure and punctuation
How well have you used sentences and punctuation?

The writing uses a variety of sentence structures, including complex sentences (e.g. *It has a fleece for extra warmth which can be zipped up if needed.*) There is consistent use of tense and pronouns. Some descriptive phrases are used (e.g. ... *elastic cuffs to help stop draughts getting inside ...*). There is correct use of capital letters and full stops. There has been an attempt to use commas in sentences although from the two instances (one correct the other incorrect) and the lack of any other punctuation within sentences, it is not possible to say that the child knows how to use punctuation in this way. For this reason, 4 rather than 5 marks have been awarded to this writing for Strand A. *(4 marks)*

Strand B – text structure and organisation
How effectively have you structured and organised your writing?

The opening is suitable, providing a brief overview of the context and the report. This writing has clearly defined beginning, middle and end sections. The events (the positive and negative aspects of the coat) are handled separately, and the spatial relationship between the coat and its features is touched upon (e.g. *a mobile pocket in the inside layer*). Sentences are grouped to distinguish feelings about the positive and negative aspects, and paragraphs clearly mark the beginning, middle and end sections. The context is given and this is continued throughout the writing with subtle reminders that this is a review of a product by a group of children (e.g. ... *some not so great things; ... Overall we thought ...*). The writing does not really have any variety in its structure and organisation (in the mood, apart from separate paragraphs for positive and negative aspects, or in the use of connectives). This writing therefore merits no greater than 5 marks. *(5 marks)*

Strand C – composition and effect
How effectively have you written the report?

This report is well paced – it makes relevant points throughout and does not stray from the main theme. The ending is weak and, although related to the rest of the report, requires more (albeit brief) reference to the main points. There are clear links between various points (e.g. discussing the zip up fleece then going on to mention the outer waterproof layer ... *and both layers are made of lightweight material ...*) and points are developed (e.g. providing a reason for not liking the safety light ... *We thought it might get broken ...*). Detail to help the reader is provided through giving the context although comparison to other items (e.g. a standard coat) would enhance the report. This writing matches the descriptions to just enable it to gain 8 marks, although further examples of all of the above points would make a stronger case, and a livelier, more convincing argument would take it up to 9 or 10 marks. *(8 marks)*

Strand F – handwriting
How neatly have you written during the longer task?

Most of the letters are the correct size (although the letter f is consistently poor) and the writing is mostly joined. The spacing between words and letters is appropriate but not quite even. There is evidence of a personal style developing but this handwriting merits 2 rather than 3 marks. *(2 marks)*

My class have been testing the new 2 in 1 super coat and we think it is very good and very useful. We have found some great things and some not so great things that could be better.

Repetitive sentence and ideas structure.

The good bits about the coat are that it is for both boys and girls. It has a fleece for extra warmth which can be zipped out is needed. The outer layer is waterproof and both layers are made of lightweight meterial to make it better to wear. The reflective strips mean you can be seen in the dark. Both layers have elastic cuffs to help stop draughts getting inside the coat. Finally it has a mobile pocket in the inside layer to help keep your phone safe.

Complex sentence.

Descriptive phrase.

The three things we thought that were not so great, were the safety light. We thought it might get broken and may add weight. Although the coat has a fixed hood, a removable one would add greater flexibility. The coat has 4 pockets in each layer with buttons but it may be better to use zips.

Overall we thought it was a good coat that could be improved with a few slight design changes.

Clear conclusion but with little extra detail.

Clear structure: paragraphs for good and bad features.

Sample Marking of the Set B Short Writing Test – "On Your Bike"

Strand D – sentence structure, punctuation and text organisation
How well have you organised your writing and used grammar and punctuation?

The sections of this writing are organised into paragraphs containing different angles on the theme. There is evidence of a good variety of sentence structures and lengths. Simple joining words are used (e.g. *if, plus, then*) and most sentences are grammatically correct. Punctuation is mostly correct and an attempt has been made at punctuation within sentences, although better use of this would enhance the writing. A further benefit would be the use of more imaginative connectives. This writing merits 2 rather than 3 marks.

(2 marks)

Strand E – composition and effect
How effectively have you written the shorter task?

The writing makes a direct appeal to its intended audience and gives a fairly clear picture of the subject and circumstances. There is an appropriate amount of information given but some reiteration of the points made in the prompt would help to take this writing into a higher band. Short descriptive phrases are in evidence (*They're quiet, and they don't pollute the environment ...; Cars pollute, bikes don't*). These points also provide significant and helpful detail for the reader, and all of the points made are sequenced properly. Unfortunately, a lack of emotion in the writing reduces the persuasive effects of the letter, which merits 4 marks.

(4 marks)

Dear Editor,
I am writing to disagree with Anne Eastwood about her saying that cycling is wrong.

Bikes arn't a nuisance, they keep you fit and healthy, plus you can have a lot of fun on them. Cycling will keep you fit, If you cycle regulary.

What is wrong with bikes?
They're quiet, and they don't pollute the environment with nasty fumes! They are safe if you wear a helmet too. and ride sensibly.

If you put lots of cyclepaths down then the cyclists wont disturb drivers of cars/lorrys or trucks. Cars pollute, bikes don't.

If bikes were banned then the world would just be a polluted peice of land. Please don't ban bikes.
Yours sincerely
        Michael Gibson

Clear intent.

Uncertain use of punctuation.

Simple connectives but they don't help to list arguments.

Powerful statement.

Spelling Test Passages

Belgian Connection

In 1815 the Duke of Wellington **defeated** the French army of Napoleon near the **village** of Waterloo, a few kilometres from Brussels in Belgium.

The Battle of Waterloo was not only **seen** as a great **victory** for the British but it also gave its name to a **central** London railway station.

Waterloo station was **opened** on 11 July 1848 by London South West Railway. Over the **following** 50 years many more parts were added as a result of the **dramatic** increase in the number of railway lines.

Between 1902 and 1922 the station was completely rebuilt and had its **official** opening in March 1922. A Victory Arch, representing war and **peace**, was **incorporated** into the façade. This commemorated workers who died in World War I.

As the **twentieth** century came to a close, Waterloo was **enlarged** as it became London's main **connection** with the railways of Europe **through** the Channel Tunnel. The station **boasts** the largest roof area of any railway station in the UK and has shops, food outlets and even a **cinema**. Remarkably, the station now also has a new link with Belgium. **Each** day the Eurostar **service** runs up to nine trains a day from London Waterloo to Brussels.

Cool Sports

Despite being cold and hard, ice has become **widely** used by humans for many sports.
They all **require** nerve and skill to both maintain balance and **compete** at the same time.

Ice-skating involves **propelling** yourself across ice using **special** bladed boots **known** as skates.
It is an **extremely** popular sport throughout the world and has several forms.

Speed skating involves races on a frozen **circuit** over distances of up to 10,000 **metres**. The races are much quicker than **similar** races on an athletics track. At the 1980 Winter Olympics, the speed skater Eric Heiden won five gold medals, a **feat** never previously **achieved** in the sport.

Figure skating is an event for individuals or mixed pairs. The **competitors** skate to music while **attempting** to perform a range of spectacular and **accurate** moves such as spins and jumps. They are then **judged** for technical merit, required elements and **presentation**.

Ice hockey is a team game **played** on ice. It is regarded as the fastest team sport in the world with the players hitting the puck at well over 100 km per hour. With the pace of the game and **passionate** crowds the **action** often gets very exciting and sometimes violent.

Marking the Spelling Test

After completion of the test, total up the number of words spelt correctly. This total for the Spelling Test is converted into marks that contribute to the overall level for Writing. Marks should be given as indicated. Enter the marks on the marking grid on page 8.

Number of correct words	1–3	4–6	7–9	10–12	13–15	16–18	19–20
Marks	1	2	3	4	5	6	7